Mental Maths Every Day for ages 8–9

Dear Parents,

Thank you for buying this copy of *Mental Maths Every Day 8–9*, one of a six book series of maths practice books for primary aged children.

Why is mental maths so important?
All children need to know number facts so that they can remember them instantly when working on more complex aspects of maths. Children who are confident in mental maths also tend to be more confident when faced with money, time, measurements and other mathematical concepts.

This book is designed to boost children's confidence by giving them plenty of practice in quick calculations. The calculations become progressively more difficult as the child works through the book. Don't be surprised if the first few pages seem easy – it's still important that your child completes them. Your child will find some of the other pages very difficult but this is quite normal too; just be on hand to provide help and guidance when needed.

How do I use the book?
Each page of this book is split into columns of questions that have been specially devised for children aged 8–9. Using a stopwatch or clock, ask your child to do as many questions as possible from the first column in exactly one minute. Allow your child to use fingers or counters if she/he needs to. Prompt your child to look very carefully at each question, paying special attention to the mathematical symbol – for example, whether it is an instruction to add or subtract.

At the end of the minute, mark the questions with your child and write down the score for the column in the score box. To save time, the answers are provided on pages 30 to 32. Your child probably won't have time to complete all the questions in the column but praise her/him for trying hard and doing as many as possible. Take the opportunity to discuss any mistakes that have been made and show the child how to do any questions that have been missed out. When she/he is ready your child can complete the next column and try and improve the score. Don't worry if it doesn't improve immediately – 'practice makes perfect' and the improvement in performance will take place sooner or later. Remember that the best way to help is to give lots of praise for success and lots of support where the child is experiencing any difficulty. I do hope that your child enjoys working through the activities.

Andrew Brodie

Contents

Adding numbers up to 20

See if you can answer each set of 15 questions in one minute.

6 + 8 = 14	13 + 4 = 17	2 + 14 = 16	13 + 4 = 17
4 + 9 = 13	19 + 1 = 20	16 + 3 = 19	6 + 12 = 18
11 + 7 = 18	14 + 3 = 17	15 + 2 = 17	15 + 2 = 17
15 + 2 = 17	7 + 8 = 15	1 + 8 = 9	11 + 1 = 12
11 + 1 = 12	4 + 12 = 16	8 + 7 = 15	7 + 8 = 15
13 + 4 = 17	16 + 2 = 18	17 + 2 = 19	14 + 3 = 17
4 + 14 = 18	10 + 6 = 16	1 + 16 = 17	2 + 11 = 13
1 + 8 = 9	2 + 17 = 19	8 + 12 = 20	9 + 1 = 10
7 + 13 = 20	12 + 6 = 18	15 + 3 = 18	10 + 6 = 16
6 + 9 = 15	14 + 5 = 19	6 + 6 = 12	2 + 17 = 19
14 + 3 = 17	1 + 12 = 13	2 + 7 = 9	14 + 6 = 20
12 + 1 = 13	10 + 7 = 17	5 + 12 = 17	4 + 12 = 16
2 + 11 = 13	5 + 15 = 20	3 + 14 = 17	16 + 2 = 18
9 + 1 = 10	3 + 2 = 5	8 + 4 = 12	8 + 12 = 20
6 + 12 = 18	9 + 5 = 14	2 + 16 = 18	13 + 6 = 18
Score 15/15 1m 16s	Score 15/15 1m 19s	Score 15/15 1m 31s	Score

Subtracting numbers up to 20

See if you can answer each set of 15 questions in one minute.

12 - 7 =	5
15 - 3 =	12
11 - 4 =	7
18 - 9 =	9
11 - 5 =	6
19 - 7 =	2
10 - 6 =	4
15 - 11 =	4
8 - 3 =	5
17 - 9 =	8
15 - 5 =	10
13 - 6 =	7
19 - 8 =	11
6 - 5 =	1
20 - 3 =	17

Score 15/15

7 - 4 =	
20 - 16 =	
10 - 7 =	
17 - 1 =	
13 - 10 =	
19 - 5 =	
12 - 4 =	
11 - 8 =	
14 - 2 =	
6 - 1 =	
17 - 7 =	
19 - 4 =	
15 - 13 =	
19 - 11 =	
13 - 4 =	

Score

10 - 1 =	
17 - 5 =	
14 - 6 =	
19 - 4 =	
12 - 2 =	
9 - 5 =	
14 - 11 =	
19 - 8 =	
8 - 4 =	
18 - 13 =	
19 - 6 =	
15 - 12 =	
13 - 4 =	
16 - 11 =	
18 - 10 =	

Score

15 - 11 =	
6 - 1 =	
10 - 6 =	
15 - 13 =	
19 - 11 =	
11 - 5 =	
19 - 4 =	
17 - 7 =	
19 - 7 =	
13 - 4 =	
9 - 5 =	
19 - 4 =	
14 - 11 =	
19 - 8 =	
12 - 7 =	

Score

Adding and subtracting up to 20

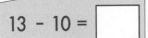

See if you can answer each set of 15 questions in one minute.

13 - 10 =	3 + 2 =	16 + 2 =	15 - 13 =
16 + 3 =	20 - 16 =	10 - 7 =	16 + 2 =
19 - 5 =	7 + 13 =	7 + 8 =	19 - 11 =
9 + 5 =	13 - 6 =	17 - 1 =	10 + 6 =
17 - 9 =	5 + 15 =	5 + 12 =	15 - 11 =
15 + 2 =	14 - 6 =	16 - 11 =	8 + 12 =
15 - 5 =	2 + 17 =	1 + 8 =	2 + 17 =
1 + 16 =	19 - 4 =	18 - 10 =	6 - 1 =
12 - 4 =	8 + 12 =	2 + 7 =	9 + 1 =
4 + 12 =	9 - 5 =	14 - 11 =	10 - 6 =
10 - 1 =	6 + 6 =	2 + 14 =	10 + 6 =
15 + 3 =	15 - 11 =	19 - 8 =	11 - 5 =
10 + 6 =	19 + 1 =	14 + 3 =	4 + 12 =
17 - 5 =	8 - 3 =	8 - 4 =	19 - 4 =
6 - 5 =	19 - 8 =	6 + 9 =	13 + 6 =
Score	Score	Score	Score

For answers see page 30

5

The 2 times table

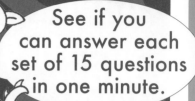

See if you can answer each set of 15 questions in one minute.

0 × 2 =	5 × 2 =	7 × 2 =	9 × 2 =
1 × 2 =	4 × 2 =	5 × 2 =	3 × 2 =
2 × 2 =	8 × 2 =	10 × 2 =	0 × 2 =
3 × 2 =	10 × 2 =	0 × 2 =	5 × 2 =
4 × 2 =	1 × 2 =	3 × 2 =	7 × 2 =
5 × 2 =	3 × 2 =	9 × 2 =	10 × 2 =
6 × 2 =	7 × 2 =	6 × 2 =	6 × 2 =
7 × 2 =	9 × 2 =	2 × 2 =	4 × 2 =
8 × 2 =	6 × 2 =	4 × 2 =	1 × 2 =
9 × 2 =	0 × 2 =	8 × 2 =	8 × 2 =
10 × 2 =	2 × 2 =	1 × 2 =	2 × 2 =
14 ÷ 2 =	16 ÷ 2 =	2 ÷ 2 =	10 ÷ 2 =
4 ÷ 2 =	6 ÷ 2 =	12 ÷ 2 =	6 ÷ 2 =
6 ÷ 2 =	10 ÷ 2 =	4 ÷ 2 =	8 ÷ 2 =
18 ÷ 2 =	8 ÷ 2 =	18 ÷ 2 =	16 ÷ 2 =
Score	Score	Score	Score

The 3 times table

See if you can answer each set of 15 questions in one minute.

0 x 3 =	4 x 3 =	9 x 3 =	5 x 3 =
1 x 3 =	6 x 3 =	4 x 3 =	7 x 3 =
2 x 3 =	1 x 3 =	2 x 3 =	0 x 3 =
3 x 3 =	9 x 3 =	8 x 3 =	3 x 3 =
4 x 3 =	7 x 3 =	6 x 3 =	10 x 3 =
5 x 3 =	2 x 3 =	0 x 3 =	8 x 3 =
6 x 3 =	8 x 3 =	5 x 3 =	2 x 3 =
7 x 3 =	0 x 3 =	1 x 3 =	4 x 3 =
8 x 3 =	3 x 3 =	10 x 3 =	6 x 3 =
9 x 3 =	10 x 3 =	7 x 3 =	1 x 3 =
10 x 3 =	5 x 3 =	3 x 3 =	9 x 3 =
24 ÷ 3 =	30 ÷ 3 =	21 ÷ 3 =	6 ÷ 3 =
12 ÷ 3 =	6 ÷ 3 =	15 ÷ 3 =	12 ÷ 3 =
18 ÷ 3 =	3 ÷ 3 =	12 ÷ 3 =	3 ÷ 3 =
9 ÷ 3 =	27 ÷ 3 =	24 ÷ 3 =	21 ÷ 3 =
Score	Score	Score	Score

For answers see page 30

Adding one-digit numbers to two-digit numbers

See if you can answer each set of 15 questions in one minute.

52 + 6 =	42 + 7 =	31 + 4 =	55 + 4 =
63 + 4 =	55 + 2 =	62 + 7 =	73 + 1 =
91 + 2 =	21 + 9 =	49 + 1 =	82 + 3 =
46 + 1 =	61 + 6 =	22 + 4 =	60 + 9 =
72 + 5 =	33 + 4 =	55 + 3 =	41 + 4 =
12 + 7 =	72 + 5 =	72 + 5 =	92 + 6 =
21 + 8 =	87 + 2 =	81 + 6 =	88 + 1 =
33 + 6 =	11 + 6 =	90 + 5 =	21 + 7 =
51 + 3 =	94 + 5 =	25 + 3 =	15 + 3 =
48 + 1 =	31 + 5 =	16 + 2 =	51 + 3 =
75 + 3 =	40 + 6 =	32 + 7 =	63 + 4 =
64 + 4 =	51 + 8 =	73 + 6 =	44 + 2 =
93 + 6 =	82 + 4 =	52 + 4 =	72 + 5 =
82 + 4 =	64 + 5 =	66 + 3 =	66 + 3 =
30 + 8 =	22 + 6 =	42 + 3 =	18 + 2 =
Score	Score	Score	Score

For answers see page 30

The 4 times table

See if you can answer each set of 15 questions in one minute.

0 x 4 =	4 x 4 =	9 x 4 =	2 x 4 =
1 x 4 =	0 x 4 =	1 x 4 =	7 x 4 =
2 x 4 =	7 x 4 =	3 x 4 =	10 x 4 =
3 x 4 =	5 x 4 =	6 x 4 =	3 x 4 =
4 x 4 =	10 x 4 =	5 x 4 =	1 x 4 =
5 x 4 =	8 x 4 =	4 x 4 =	6 x 4 =
6 x 4 =	1 x 4 =	0 x 4 =	9 x 4 =
7 x 4 =	3 x 4 =	10 x 4 =	5 x 4 =
8 x 4 =	9 x 4 =	2 x 4 =	8 x 4 =
9 x 4 =	2 x 4 =	8 x 4 =	4 x 4 =
10 x 4 =	6 x 4 =	7 x 4 =	0 x 4 =
36 ÷ 4 =	4 ÷ 4 =	20 ÷ 4 =	40 ÷ 4 =
12 ÷ 4 =	16 ÷ 4 =	28 ÷ 4 =	12 ÷ 4 =
8 ÷ 4 =	24 ÷ 4 =	16 ÷ 4 =	4 ÷ 4 =
40 ÷ 4 =	32 ÷ 4 =	8 ÷ 4 =	36 ÷ 4 =
Score	Score	Score	Score

For answers see page 30

The 5 times table

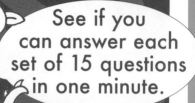

See if you can answer each set of 15 questions in one minute.

0 x 5 =

1 x 5 =

2 x 5 =

3 x 5 =

4 x 5 =

5 x 5 =

6 x 5 =

7 x 5 =

8 x 5 =

9 x 5 =

10 x 5 =

40 ÷ 5 =

20 ÷ 5 =

5 ÷ 5 =

15 ÷ 5 =

Score

2 x 5 =

6 x 5 =

9 x 5 =

10 x 5 =

0 x 5 =

3 x 5 =

8 x 5 =

4 x 5 =

1 x 5 =

5 x 5 =

7 x 5 =

50 ÷ 5 =

30 ÷ 5 =

45 ÷ 5 =

25 ÷ 5 =

Score

7 x 5 =

0 x 5 =

4 x 5 =

1 x 5 =

9 x 5 =

5 x 5 =

3 x 5 =

6 x 5 =

10 x 5 =

8 x 5 =

2 x 5 =

10 ÷ 5 =

35 ÷ 5 =

20 ÷ 5 =

40 ÷ 5 =

Score

0 x 5 =

8 x 5 =

5 x 5 =

3 x 5 =

1 x 5 =

10 x 5 =

2 x 5 =

4 x 5 =

6 x 5 =

9 x 5 =

7 x 5 =

5 ÷ 5 =

15 ÷ 5 =

50 ÷ 5 =

25 ÷ 5 =

Score

For answers see page 30

Subtracting two-digit numbers from two-digit numbers

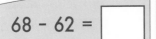

See if you can answer each set of 15 questions in one minute.

68 – 62 =	98 – 96 =	46 – 41 =	56 – 53 =
86 – 81 =	73 – 72 =	75 – 70 =	87 – 82 =
47 – 41 =	66 – 61 =	89 – 83 =	61 – 60 =
56 – 52 =	49 – 42 =	24 – 21 =	94 – 92 =
39 – 37 =	55 – 53 =	65 – 63 =	45 – 42 =
99 – 91 =	84 – 80 =	98 – 93 =	37 – 35 =
73 – 71 =	19 – 18 =	72 – 71 =	84 – 83 =
25 – 24 =	25 – 23 =	88 – 82 =	97 – 90 =
67 – 63 =	79 – 75 =	49 – 45 =	27 – 23 =
49 – 42 =	94 – 92 =	36 – 33 =	47 – 41 =
88 – 83 =	87 – 83 =	28 – 26 =	54 – 51 =
76 – 71 =	46 – 41 =	18 – 17 =	33 – 32 =
95 – 94 =	68 – 65 =	55 – 50 =	29 – 20 =
58 – 54 =	36 – 31 =	67 – 62 =	66 – 64 =
37 – 30 =	29 – 28 =	41 – 40 =	18 – 12 =
Score	Score	Score	Score

For answers see page 30

The 6 times table

See if you can answer each set of 15 questions in one minute.

0 × 6 =	2 × 6 =	5 × 6 =	1 × 6 =
1 × 6 =	7 × 6 =	1 × 6 =	9 × 6 =
2 × 6 =	0 × 6 =	10 × 6 =	4 × 6 =
3 × 6 =	10 × 6 =	8 × 6 =	2 × 6 =
4 × 6 =	3 × 6 =	4 × 6 =	5 × 6 =
5 × 6 =	4 × 6 =	3 × 6 =	7 × 6 =
6 × 6 =	9 × 6 =	9 × 6 =	0 × 6 =
7 × 6 =	1 × 6 =	6 × 6 =	3 × 6 =
8 × 6 =	5 × 6 =	2 × 6 =	8 × 6 =
9 × 6 =	8 × 6 =	0 × 6 =	10 × 6 =
10 × 6 =	6 × 6 =	7 × 6 =	6 × 6 =
48 ÷ 6 =	60 ÷ 6 =	6 ÷ 6 =	54 ÷ 6 =
12 ÷ 6 =	42 ÷ 6 =	36 ÷ 6 =	42 ÷ 6 =
30 ÷ 6 =	24 ÷ 6 =	48 ÷ 6 =	12 ÷ 6 =
54 ÷ 6 =	18 ÷ 6 =	60 ÷ 6 =	30 ÷ 6 =
Score	Score	Score	Score

For answers see page 31

The 7 times table

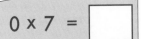

See if you can answer each set of 15 questions in one minute.

0 x 7 =	2 x 7 =	5 x 7 =	4 x 7 =
1 x 7 =	5 x 7 =	9 x 7 =	1 x 7 =
2 x 7 =	9 x 7 =	0 x 7 =	10 x 7 =
3 x 7 =	0 x 7 =	4 x 7 =	2 x 7 =
4 x 7 =	6 x 7 =	2 x 7 =	9 x 7 =
5 x 7 =	3 x 7 =	6 x 7 =	7 x 7 =
6 x 7 =	1 x 7 =	1 x 7 =	3 x 7 =
7 x 7 =	10 x 7 =	3 x 7 =	0 x 7 =
8 x 7 =	8 x 7 =	10 x 7 =	5 x 7 =
9 x 7 =	4 x 7 =	7 x 7 =	8 x 7 =
10 x 7 =	7 x 7 =	8 x 7 =	6 x 7 =
49 ÷ 7 =	14 ÷ 7 =	42 ÷ 7 =	70 ÷ 7 =
56 ÷ 7 =	28 ÷ 7 =	63 ÷ 7 =	56 ÷ 7 =
7 ÷ 7 =	70 ÷ 7 =	7 ÷ 7 =	14 ÷ 7 =
35 ÷ 7 =	21 ÷ 7 =	35 ÷ 7 =	49 ÷ 7 =
Score	Score	Score	Score

For answers see page 31

Adding two-digit numbers to two-digit numbers

See if you can answer each set of 15 questions in one minute.

18 + 12 =	39 + 11 =	59 + 11 =	54 + 16 =
41 + 19 =	45 + 15 =	63 + 17 =	63 + 17 =
36 + 14 =	68 + 12 =	78 + 12 =	45 + 15 =
52 + 18 =	32 + 18 =	65 + 15 =	89 + 11 =
66 + 14 =	46 + 14 =	42 + 18 =	21 + 19 =
75 + 15 =	51 + 19 =	61 + 19 =	47 + 13 =
39 + 11 =	24 + 16 =	34 + 16 =	26 + 14 =
42 + 18 =	79 + 11 =	22 + 18 =	12 + 18 =
54 + 16 =	57 + 13 =	57 + 13 =	29 + 11 =
67 + 13 =	62 + 18 =	39 + 11 =	58 + 12 =
72 + 18 =	47 + 13 =	85 + 15 =	71 + 19 =
28 + 12 =	74 + 16 =	24 + 16 =	57 + 13 =
35 + 15 =	65 + 15 =	36 + 14 =	64 + 16 =
14 + 16 =	49 + 11 =	52 + 18 =	39 + 11 =
29 + 11 =	38 + 12 =	67 + 13 =	23 + 17 =
Score	Score	Score	Score

For answers see page 31

The 8 times table

See if you can answer each set of 15 questions in one minute.

0 x 8 =	
1 x 8 =	
2 x 8 =	
3 x 8 =	
4 x 8 =	
5 x 8 =	
6 x 8 =	
7 x 8 =	
8 x 8 =	
9 x 8 =	
10 x 8 =	
64 ÷ 8 =	
16 ÷ 8 =	
24 ÷ 8 =	
56 ÷ 8 =	

Score

2 x 8 =	
10 x 8 =	
3 x 8 =	
7 x 8 =	
6 x 8 =	
4 x 8 =	
9 x 8 =	
1 x 8 =	
8 x 8 =	
0 x 8 =	
5 x 8 =	
8 ÷ 8 =	
40 ÷ 8 =	
32 ÷ 8 =	
72 ÷ 8 =	

Score

5 x 8 =	
3 x 8 =	
1 x 8 =	
6 x 8 =	
0 x 8 =	
4 x 8 =	
8 x 8 =	
2 x 8 =	
10 x 8 =	
7 x 8 =	
9 x 8 =	
80 ÷ 8 =	
48 ÷ 8 =	
24 ÷ 8 =	
16 ÷ 8 =	

Score

9 x 8 =	
2 x 8 =	
5 x 8 =	
10 x 8 =	
3 x 8 =	
1 x 8 =	
4 x 8 =	
8 x 8 =	
0 x 8 =	
6 x 8 =	
7 x 8 =	
64 ÷ 8 =	
16 ÷ 8 =	
56 ÷ 8 =	
8 ÷ 8 =	

Score

For answers see page 31

The 9 times table

See if you can answer each set of 15 questions in one minute.

0 x 9 =	
1 x 9 =	
2 x 9 =	
3 x 9 =	
4 x 9 =	
5 x 9 =	
6 x 9 =	
7 x 9 =	
8 x 9 =	
9 x 9 =	
10 x 9 =	
90 ÷ 9 =	
9 ÷ 9 =	
18 ÷ 9 =	
63 ÷ 9 =	

Score

2 x 9 =	
5 x 9 =	
8 x 9 =	
0 x 9 =	
6 x 9 =	
3 x 9 =	
1 x 9 =	
10 x 9 =	
4 x 9 =	
7 x 9 =	
9 x 9 =	
27 ÷ 9 =	
45 ÷ 9 =	
72 ÷ 9 =	
36 ÷ 9 =	

Score

9 x 9 =	
4 x 9 =	
2 x 9 =	
5 x 9 =	
1 x 9 =	
6 x 9 =	
3 x 9 =	
8 x 9 =	
0 x 9 =	
7 x 9 =	
10 x 9 =	
54 ÷ 9 =	
81 ÷ 9 =	
9 ÷ 9 =	
18 ÷ 9 =	

Score

4 x 9 =	
6 x 9 =	
0 x 9 =	
1 x 9 =	
8 x 9 =	
7 x 9 =	
10 x 9 =	
5 x 9 =	
3 x 9 =	
2 x 9 =	
9 x 9 =	
72 ÷ 9 =	
63 ÷ 9 =	
18 ÷ 9 =	
27 ÷ 9 =	

Score

For answers see page 31

Subtracting two-digit numbers from multiples of 10

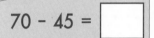

See if you can answer each set of 15 questions in one minute.

70 − 45 =	
80 − 68 =	
30 − 16 =	
40 − 34 =	
50 − 19 =	
60 − 27 =	
90 − 55 =	
20 − 18 =	
30 − 25 =	
40 − 12 =	
60 − 45 =	
70 − 38 =	
50 − 24 =	
20 − 16 =	
80 − 34 =	

Score

90 − 45 =	
30 − 15 =	
80 − 23 =	
50 − 44 =	
70 − 67 =	
40 − 34 =	
60 − 19 =	
20 − 12 =	
30 − 24 =	
80 − 45 =	
90 − 34 =	
60 − 52 =	
80 − 51 =	
70 − 64 =	
50 − 39 =	

Score

20 − 11 =	
40 − 24 =	
60 − 45 =	
70 − 32 =	
80 − 64 =	
50 − 29 =	
90 − 36 =	
30 − 25 =	
40 − 38 =	
60 − 52 =	
80 − 66 =	
50 − 35 =	
90 − 56 =	
70 − 37 =	
60 − 45 =	

Score

30 − 12 =	
50 − 43 =	
90 − 76 =	
40 − 23 =	
70 − 56 =	
60 − 45 =	
80 − 22 =	
20 − 16 =	
60 − 34 =	
50 − 13 =	
70 − 56 =	
90 − 63 =	
50 − 37 =	
70 − 58 =	
50 − 39 =	

Score

For answers see page 31

Multiplying by 10

See if you can answer each set of 15 questions in one minute.

10 × 6 =	10 × 44 =	10 × 53 =	10 × 7 =
10 × 8 =	10 × 15 =	10 × 9 =	10 × 84 =
10 × 2 =	10 × 3 =	10 × 10 =	10 × 27 =
10 × 37 =	10 × 70 =	10 × 65 =	10 × 12 =
10 × 11 =	10 × 26 =	10 × 74 =	10 × 67 =
10 × 31 =	10 × 57 =	10 × 18 =	10 × 89 =
10 × 1 =	10 × 63 =	10 × 36 =	10 × 24 =
10 × 17 =	10 × 7 =	10 × 99 =	10 × 6 =
10 × 4 =	10 × 34 =	10 × 47 =	10 × 46 =
10 × 56 =	10 × 21 =	10 × 12 =	10 × 68 =
10 × 0 =	10 × 45 =	10 × 77 =	10 × 92 =
10 × 23 =	10 × 97 =	10 × 38 =	10 × 83 =
10 × 29 =	10 × 9 =	10 × 4 =	10 × 49 =
10 × 5 =	10 × 39 =	10 × 33 =	10 × 58 =
10 × 50 =	10 × 61 =	10 × 78 =	10 × 95 =
Score	Score	Score	Score

For answers see page 31

Dividing by 10

See if you can answer each set of 15 questions in one minute.

70 ÷ 10 =	80 ÷ 10 =	70 ÷ 10 =	30 ÷ 10 =
230 ÷ 10 =	220 ÷ 10 =	680 ÷ 10 =	760 ÷ 10 =
20 ÷ 10 =	40 ÷ 10 =	590 ÷ 10 =	170 ÷ 10 =
350 ÷ 10 =	470 ÷ 10 =	310 ÷ 10 =	940 ÷ 10 =
920 ÷ 10 =	910 ÷ 10 =	850 ÷ 10 =	620 ÷ 10 =
60 ÷ 10 =	260 ÷ 10 =	30 ÷ 10 =	510 ÷ 10 =
490 ÷ 10 =	50 ÷ 10 =	540 ÷ 10 =	80 ÷ 10 =
110 ÷ 10 =	710 ÷ 10 =	970 ÷ 10 =	450 ÷ 10 =
370 ÷ 10 =	460 ÷ 10 =	360 ÷ 10 =	890 ÷ 10 =
530 ÷ 10 =	980 ÷ 10 =	720 ÷ 10 =	420 ÷ 10 =
640 ÷ 10 =	650 ÷ 10 =	610 ÷ 10 =	770 ÷ 10 =
780 ÷ 10 =	320 ÷ 10 =	950 ÷ 10 =	960 ÷ 10 =
750 ÷ 10 =	810 ÷ 10 =	290 ÷ 10 =	210 ÷ 10 =
820 ÷ 10 =	430 ÷ 10 =	40 ÷ 10 =	880 ÷ 10 =
190 ÷ 10 =	740 ÷ 10 =	830 ÷ 10 =	340 ÷ 10 =
Score	Score	Score	Score

Multiplying and dividing by 10

See if you can answer each set of 15 questions in one minute.

470 ÷ 10 =	710 ÷ 10 =	680 ÷ 10 =	10 × 43 =
10 × 36 =	10 × 17 =	10 × 50 =	940 ÷ 10 =
580 ÷ 10 =	320 ÷ 10 =	10 × 0 =	620 ÷ 10 =
10 × 38 =	780 ÷ 10 =	370 ÷ 10 =	10 × 7 =
10 × 70 =	10 × 96 =	10 × 15 =	510 ÷ 10 =
50 ÷ 10 =	810 ÷ 10 =	530 ÷ 10 =	10 × 84 =
10 × 47 =	10 × 7 =	640 ÷ 10 =	280 ÷ 10 =
220 ÷ 10 =	190 ÷ 10 =	10 × 57 =	450 ÷ 10 =
10 × 56 =	10 × 9 =	750 ÷ 10 =	10 × 89 =
840 ÷ 10 =	70 ÷ 10 =	30 ÷ 10 =	890 ÷ 10 =
10 × 4 =	10 × 26 =	10 × 3 =	10 × 75 =
10 × 77 =	430 ÷ 10 =	850 ÷ 10 =	10 × 27 =
910 ÷ 10 =	10 × 12 =	10 × 63 =	420 ÷ 10 =
10 × 44 =	740 ÷ 10 =	540 ÷ 10 =	10 × 24 =
260 ÷ 10 =	10 × 39 =	10 × 1 =	770 ÷ 10 =
Score	Score	Score	Score

For answers see page 31

Adding one-digit numbers to two-digit numbers

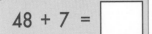

See if you can answer each set of 15 questions in one minute.

48 + 7 =	33 + 9 =	47 + 4 =	36 + 5 =
59 + 6 =	67 + 4 =	85 + 6 =	48 + 4 =
82 + 9 =	59 + 2 =	39 + 5 =	78 + 6 =
36 + 5 =	45 + 6 =	62 + 9 =	37 + 7 =
55 + 7 =	38 + 3 =	78 + 3 =	87 + 5 =
42 + 9 =	77 + 5 =	29 + 4 =	56 + 5 =
34 + 7 =	44 + 8 =	57 + 5 =	66 + 8 =
78 + 5 =	52 + 9 =	69 + 6 =	44 + 9 =
56 + 8 =	63 + 8 =	37 + 9 =	75 + 6 =
28 + 3 =	48 + 3 =	26 + 5 =	83 + 9 =
67 + 5 =	69 + 2 =	78 + 5 =	59 + 4 =
89 + 4 =	25 + 7 =	46 + 8 =	39 + 6 =
53 + 9 =	77 + 5 =	56 + 6 =	65 + 9 =
75 + 8 =	68 + 6 =	73 + 9 =	47 + 4 =
45 + 6 =	39 + 4 =	67 + 5 =	67 + 5 =
Score	Score	Score	Score

Subtracting one-digit numbers from two-digit numbers

See if you can answer each set of 15 questions in one minute.

92 – 6 =	54 – 5 =	65 – 7 =	23 – 9 =
81 – 8 =	82 – 5 =	34 – 5 =	44 – 5 =
71 – 4 =	63 – 7 =	71 – 3 =	84 – 6 =
51 – 4 =	78 – 9 =	45 – 8 =	72 – 6 =
12 – 7 =	21 – 2 =	78 – 9 =	95 – 9 =
33 – 9 =	65 – 7 =	35 – 6 =	25 – 7 =
46 – 8 =	33 – 8 =	42 – 6 =	45 – 8 =
57 – 8 =	86 – 7 =	55 – 8 =	71 – 2 =
84 – 5 =	44 – 9 =	82 – 3 =	53 – 4 =
77 – 9 =	52 – 4 =	56 – 9 =	24 – 5 =
31 – 3 =	24 – 6 =	44 – 7 =	61 – 7 =
66 – 8 =	81 – 5 =	31 – 6 =	48 – 9 =
74 – 8 =	72 – 3 =	64 – 5 =	62 – 3 =
32 – 5 =	85 – 9 =	73 – 8 =	77 – 9 =
45 – 7 =	45 – 7 =	41 – 5 =	52 – 5 =
Score	Score	Score	Score

For answers see page 32

Adding and subtracting up to 100

See if you can answer each set of 15 questions in one minute.

84 – 5 =	82 + 9 =	45 – 6 =	71 – 3 =
47 + 4 =	56 + 5 =	83 – 5 =	68 + 8 =
53 + 9 =	31 – 3 =	54 + 7 =	42 + 9 =
66 – 8 =	44 + 7 =	62 + 9 =	53 – 7 =
28 + 3 =	72 – 9 =	48 – 9 =	39 + 4 =
54 – 5 =	19 + 3 =	26 + 5 =	26 + 7 =
87 – 9 =	88 + 4 =	53 – 5 =	19 + 2 =
33 + 8 =	75 + 6 =	37 – 9 =	58 – 9 =
58 – 9 =	38 – 9 =	67 + 9 =	44 – 6 =
42 + 9 =	32 – 7 =	26 + 8 =	78 + 3 =
55 + 6 =	66 + 6 =	41 – 2 =	97 – 9 =
21 – 2 =	41 – 2 =	66 + 5 =	56 + 5 =
86 + 5 =	74 – 5 =	91 – 2 =	31 – 2 =
63 – 4 =	64 + 8 =	85 + 6 =	82 + 9 =
92 – 9 =	27 – 9 =	64 – 5 =	48 + 3 =
Score	Score	Score	Score

For answers see page 32

Adding three numbers together

See if you can answer each set of 15 questions in one minute.

3 + 5 + 4 =	4 + 6 + 2 =	8 + 3 + 6 =	2 + 7 + 4 =
1 + 5 + 2 =	7 + 4 + 7 =	1 + 5 + 5 =	1 + 8 + 3 =
5 + 2 + 6 =	2 + 3 + 9 =	6 + 3 + 8 =	3 + 5 + 1 =
4 + 5 + 2 =	1 + 4 + 4 =	3 + 7 + 5 =	4 + 8 + 3 =
6 + 1 + 3 =	5 + 5 + 5 =	3 + 8 + 4 =	7 + 6 + 8 =
7 + 3 + 4 =	2 + 7 + 8 =	6 + 2 + 7 =	3 + 6 + 5 =
1 + 4 + 1 =	4 + 6 + 5 =	4 + 9 + 5 =	2 + 8 + 4 =
5 + 3 + 2 =	1 + 3 + 9 =	5 + 8 + 2 =	7 + 7 + 7 =
5 + 7 + 4 =	6 + 2 + 4 =	5 + 7 + 8 =	2 + 4 + 5 =
3 + 2 + 8 =	3 + 5 + 7 =	2 + 6 + 0 =	6 + 8 + 3 =
1 + 6 + 4 =	4 + 7 + 5 =	5 + 3 + 6 =	8 + 3 + 5 =
6 + 4 + 3 =	6 + 3 + 6 =	3 + 6 + 4 =	6 + 1 + 4 =
5 + 3 + 5 =	2 + 4 + 8 =	6 + 8 + 3 =	9 + 3 + 2 =
7 + 5 + 3 =	5 + 2 + 7 =	3 + 5 + 7 =	5 + 8 + 4 =
1 + 7 + 4 =	4 + 5 + 7 =	2 + 7 + 5 =	3 + 4 + 9 =
Score	Score	Score	Score

For answers see page 32

Finding halves of even numbers

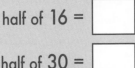

See if you can answer each set of 15 questions in one minute.

half of 16 =	half of 60 =	half of 20 =	half of 10 =
half of 30 =	half of 66 =	half of 46 =	half of 42 =
half of 2 =	half of 80 =	half of 60 =	half of 66 =
half of 44 =	half of 26 =	half of 62 =	half of 44 =
half of 28 =	half of 48 =	half of 50 =	half of 26 =
half of 8 =	half of 86 =	half of 30 =	half of 88 =
half of 12 =	half of 20 =	half of 90 =	half of 90 =
half of 80 =	half of 6 =	half of 32 =	half of 18 =
half of 24 =	half of 44 =	half of 88 =	half of 30 =
half of 32 =	half of 18 =	half of 28 =	half of 50 =
half of 60 =	half of 4 =	half of 14 =	half of 70 =
half of 80 =	half of 100 =	half of 64 =	half of 62 =
half of 90 =	half of 40 =	half of 82 =	half of 6 =
half of 22 =	half of 22 =	half of 26 =	half of 84 =
half of 46 =	half of 84 =	half of 52 =	half of 46 =
Score	Score	Score	Score

For answers see page 32

Finding doubles

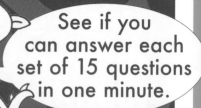

See if you can answer each set of 15 questions in one minute.

double 3 = ☐	double 6 = ☐	double 5 = ☐	double 3 = ☐
double 15 = ☐	double 8 = ☐	double 50 = ☐	double 60 = ☐
double 20 = ☐	double 50 = ☐	double 45 = ☐	double 63 = ☐
double 8 = ☐	double 80 = ☐	double 75 = ☐	double 9 = ☐
double 9 = ☐	double 60 = ☐	double 90 = ☐	double 40 = ☐
double 11 = ☐	double 18 = ☐	double 19 = ☐	double 62 = ☐
double 12 = ☐	double 31 = ☐	double 53 = ☐	double 80 = ☐
double 30 = ☐	double 4 = ☐	double 65 = ☐	double 13 = ☐
double 80 = ☐	double 24 = ☐	double 14 = ☐	double 81 = ☐
double 37 = ☐	double 99 = ☐	double 3 = ☐	double 52 = ☐
double 24 = ☐	double 40 = ☐	double 15 = ☐	double 44 = ☐
double 70 = ☐	double 83 = ☐	double 64 = ☐	double 74 = ☐
double 34 = ☐	double 22 = ☐	double 91 = ☐	double 33 = ☐
double 72 = ☐	double 21 = ☐	double 82 = ☐	double 61 = ☐
double 5 = ☐	double 75 = ☐	double 51 = ☐	double 54 = ☐
Score ☐	Score ☐	Score ☐	Score ☐

For answers see page 32

Adding multiples of 10

See if you can answer each set of 15 questions in one minute.

60 + 50 =	50 + 90 =	180 + 30 =	80 + 40 =
20 + 90 =	140 + 30 =	60 + 190 =	100 + 180 =
50 + 80 =	80 + 100 =	140 + 60 =	150 + 20 =
10 + 120 =	120 + 70 =	80 + 170 =	70 + 50 =
80 + 40 =	60 + 60 =	50 + 60 =	80 + 150 =
150 + 20 =	10 + 150 =	20 + 140 =	130 + 90 =
70 + 50 =	130 + 120 =	80 + 150 =	150 + 110 =
30 + 60 =	50 + 140 =	130 + 90 =	10 + 120 =
140 + 30 =	90 + 80 =	150 + 110 =	150 + 60 =
90 + 70 =	70 + 130 =	40 + 70 =	80 + 130 =
40 + 110 =	150 + 60 =	120 + 80 =	50 + 60 =
120 + 60 =	100 + 180 =	90 + 150 =	60 + 90 =
60 + 90 =	60 + 90 =	70 + 170 =	50 + 80 =
110 + 120 =	80 + 130 =	110 + 80 =	20 + 140 =
80 + 70 =	140 + 70 =	150 + 130 =	70 + 130 =
Score	Score	Score	Score

For answers see page 32

Subtracting multiples of 10

See if you can answer each set of 15 questions in one minute.

170 – 90 =	160 – 110 =	150 – 110 =	150 – 80 =
190 – 50 =	90 – 70 =	190 – 70 =	170 – 60 =
200 – 60 =	200 – 140 =	140 – 100 =	180 – 140 =
150 – 80 =	180 – 130 =	200 – 90 =	150 – 90 =
170 – 60 =	150 – 90 =	80 – 30 =	200 – 60 =
80 – 50 =	100 – 80 =	170 – 130 =	220 – 170 =
140 – 70 =	170 – 120 =	120 – 80 =	100 – 80 =
180 – 90 =	120 – 90 =	180 – 140 =	110 – 80 =
160 – 130 =	140 – 80 =	220 – 170 =	120 – 90 =
90 – 60 =	220 – 140 =	110 – 80 =	170 – 120 =
200 – 120 =	160 – 70 =	160 – 90 =	160 – 90 =
170 – 80 =	180 – 150 =	130 – 70 =	190 – 50 =
140 – 120 =	130 – 80 =	210 – 150 =	180 – 130 =
210 – 50 =	110 – 50 =	90 – 50 =	170 – 90 =
120 – 70 =	190 – 130 =	130 – 60 =	130 – 70 =
Score	Score	Score	Score

For answers see page 32

Adding and subtracting with multiples of 10

See if you can answer each set of 15 questions in one minute.

50 + 90 =	90 + 70 =	220 – 140 =	80 + 100 =
130 – 80 =	40 + 110 =	80 + 170 =	220 – 170 =
80 + 100 =	200 – 120 =	210 – 50 =	120 + 70 =
170 – 80 =	110 + 120 =	140 + 30 =	200 – 90 =
120 + 60 =	180 – 150 =	50 + 60 =	170 – 130 =
170 – 130 =	60 + 90 =	140 – 70 =	60 + 60 =
60 + 60 =	120 – 80 =	100 + 180 =	80 – 30 =
130 + 120 =	80 + 130 =	140 – 120 =	10 + 150 =
120 – 70 =	180 – 140 =	200 – 140 =	140 – 100 =
80 + 70 =	110 – 50 =	20 + 140 =	130 + 120 =
120 + 70 =	140 + 70 =	190 – 130 =	180 – 140 =
220 – 170 =	180 – 90 =	60 + 90 =	110 – 80 =
90 – 60 =	60 + 190 =	140 – 80 =	50 + 140 =
30 + 60 =	180 – 130 =	80 + 150 =	90 + 80 =
160 – 130 =	140 + 60 =	160 – 110 =	120 – 80 =
Score	Score	Score	Score

Page 3 — Adding numbers up to 20

Column 1	Column 2	Column 3	Column 4
14	17	16	17
13	20	19	18
18	17	17	17
17	15	9	12
12	16	15	15
17	18	19	17
18	16	17	13
9	19	20	10
20	18	18	16
15	19	12	19
17	13	9	20
13	17	17	16
13	20	17	18
10	5	12	20
18	14	18	19

Page 4 — Subtracting numbers up to 20

Column 1	Column 2	Column 3	Column 4
5	3	9	4
12	4	12	5
7	3	8	4
9	16	15	2
6	3	10	8
12	14	4	6
4	8	3	15
4	3	11	10
5	12	4	12
8	5	5	9
10	10	13	4
7	15	3	15
11	2	9	3
1	8	5	11
17	9	8	5

Page 5 — Adding and subtracting up to 20

Column 1	Column 2	Column 3	Column 4
3	5	18	2
19	4	3	18
14	20	15	8
14	7	16	16
8	20	17	4
17	8	5	20
10	19	9	19
17	15	8	5
8	20	9	10
16	4	3	4
9	12	16	16
18	4	11	6
16	20	17	16
12	5	4	15
1	11	15	19

Page 6 — The 2 times table

Column 1	Column 2	Column 3	Column 4
0	10	14	18
2	8	10	6
4	16	20	0
6	20	0	10
8	2	6	14
10	6	18	20
12	14	12	12
14	18	4	8
16	12	8	2
18	0	16	16
20	4	2	4
7	8	1	5
2	3	6	3
3	5	2	4
9	4	9	8

Page 7 — The 3 times table

Column 1	Column 2	Column 3	Column 4
0	12	27	15
3	18	12	21
6	3	6	0
9	27	24	9
12	21	18	30
15	6	0	24
18	24	15	6
21	0	3	12
24	9	30	18
27	30	21	3
30	15	9	27
8	10	7	2
4	2	5	4
6	1	4	1
3	9	8	7

Page 8 — Adding one-digit numbers to two-digit numbers

Column 1	Column 2	Column 3	Column 4
58	49	35	59
67	57	69	74
93	30	50	85
47	67	26	69
77	37	58	45
19	77	77	98
29	89	87	89
39	17	95	28
54	99	28	18
49	36	18	54
78	46	39	67
68	59	79	46
99	86	56	77
86	69	69	69
38	28	45	20

Page 9 — The 4 times table

Column 1	Column 2	Column 3	Column 4
0	16	36	8
4	0	4	28
8	28	12	40
12	20	24	12
16	40	20	4
20	32	16	24
24	4	0	36
28	12	40	20
32	36	8	32
36	8	32	16
40	24	28	0
9	1	5	10
3	4	7	3
		4	1
10	8	2	9

Page 10 — The 5 times table

Column 1	Column 2	Column 3	Column 4
0	10	35	0
5	30	0	40
10	45	20	25
15	50	5	15
20	0	45	5
25	15	25	50
30	40	15	10
35	20	30	20
40	5	50	30
45	25	40	45
50	35	10	35
8	10	2	1
4	6	7	3
1	9	4	10
3	5	8	5

Page 11 — Subtracting two-digit numbers from two-digit numbers

Column 1	Column 2	Column 3	Column 4
6	2	5	3
5	1	5	5
6	5	6	1
4	7	3	2
2	2	2	3
8	4	5	2
2	1	1	1
1	2	6	7
4	4	4	4
7	2	3	6
5	4	2	3
5	5	1	1
1	3	5	9
4	5	5	2
7	1	1	6

Page 12
The 6 times table

Column 1	Column 2	Column 3	Column 4
0	12	30	6
6	42	6	54
12	0	60	24
18	60	48	12
24	18	24	30
30	24	18	42
36	54	54	0
42	6	36	18
48	30	12	48
54	48	0	60
60	36	42	36
8	10	1	9
2	7	6	7
5	4	8	2
9	3	10	5

Page 13
The 7 times table

Column 1	Column 2	Column 3	Column 4
0	14	35	28
7	35	63	7
14	63	0	70
21	0	28	14
28	42	14	63
35	21	42	49
42	7	7	21
49	70	21	0
56	56	70	35
63	28	49	56
70	49	56	42
7	2	6	10
8	4	9	8
1	10	1	2
5	3	5	7

Page 14
Adding two-digit numbers to two-digit numbers

Column 1	Column 2	Column 3	Column 4
30	50	70	70
60	60	80	80
50	80	90	60
70	50	80	100
80	60	60	40
90	70	80	60
50	40	50	40
60	90	40	30
70	70	70	40
80	80	50	70
90	60	100	90
40	90	40	70
50	80	50	80
30	60	70	50
40	50	80	40

Page 15
The 8 times table

Column 1	Column 2	Column 3	Column 4
0	16	40	72
8	80	24	16
16	24	8	40
24	56	48	80
32	48	0	24
40	32	32	8
48	72	64	32
56	8	16	64
64	64	80	0
72	0	56	48
80	40	72	56
8	1	10	8
2	5	6	2
3	4	3	7
7	9	2	1

Page 16
The 9 times table

Column 1	Column 2	Column 3	Column 4
0	18	81	36
9	45	36	54
18	72	18	0
27	0	45	9
36	54	9	72
45	27	54	63
54	9	27	90
63	90	72	45
72	36	0	27
81	63	63	18
90	81	90	81
10	3	6	8
1	5	9	7
2	8	1	2
7	4	2	3

Page 17
Subtracting two-digit numbers from multiples of 10

Column 1	Column 2	Column 3	Column 4
25	45	9	18
12	15	16	7
14	57	15	14
6	6	38	17
31	3	16	14
33	6	21	15
35	41	54	58
2	8	5	4
5	6	2	26
28	35	8	37
15	56	14	14
32	8	15	27
26	29	34	13
4	6	33	12
46	11	15	11

Page 18
Multiplying by 10

Column 1	Column 2	Column 3	Column 4
60	440	530	70
80	150	90	840
20	30	100	270
370	700	650	120
110	260	740	670
310	570	180	890
10	630	360	240
170	70	990	60
40	340	470	460
560	210	120	680
0	450	770	920
230	970	380	830
290	90	40	490
50	390	330	580
500	610	780	950

Page 19
Dividing by 10

Column 1	Column 2	Column 3	Column 4
7	8	7	3
23	22	68	76
2	4	59	17
35	47	31	94
92	91	85	62
6	26	3	51
49	5	54	8
11	71	97	45
37	46	36	89
53	98	72	42
64	65	61	77
78	32	95	96
75	81	29	21
82	43	4	88
19	74	83	34

Page 20
Multiplying and dividing by 10

Column 1	Column 2	Column 3	Column 4
47	71	68	430
360	170	500	94
58	32	0	62
380	78	37	70
700	960	150	51
5	81	53	840
470	70	64	28
22	19	570	45
560	90	75	890
84	7	3	89
40	260	30	750
770	43	85	270
91	120	630	42
440	74	54	240
26	390	10	77

Page 21
Adding one-digit numbers to two-digit numbers

Column 1	Column 2	Column 3	Column 4
55	42	51	41
65	71	91	52
91	61	44	84
41	51	71	44
62	41	81	92
51	82	33	61
41	52	62	74
83	61	75	53
64	71	46	81
31	51	31	92
72	71	83	63
93	32	54	45
62	82	62	74
83	74	82	51
51	43	72	72

Page 22
Subtracting one-digit numbers from two-digit numbers

Column 1	Column 2	Column 3	Column 4
86	49	58	14
73	77	29	39
67	56	68	78
47	69	37	66
5	19	69	86
24	58	29	18
38	25	36	37
49	79	47	69
79	35	79	49
68	48	47	19
28	18	37	54
58	76	25	39
66	69	59	59
27	76	65	68
38	38	36	47

Page 23
Adding and subtracting up to 100

Column 1	Column 2	Column 3	Column 4
79	91	39	68
51	61	78	76
62	28	61	51
58	51	71	46
31	63	39	43
49	22	31	33
78	92	48	21
41	81	28	49
49	29	76	38
51	25	34	81
61	72	39	88
19	39	71	61
91	69	89	29
59	72	91	91
83	18	59	51

Page 24
Adding three numbers together

Column 1	Column 2	Column 3	Column 4
12	12	17	13
8	18	11	12
13	14	17	9
11	9	15	15
10	15	15	21
14	17	15	14
6	15	18	14
10	13	15	21
16	12	20	11
13	15	8	17
11	16	14	16
13	15	13	11
13	14	17	14
15	14	15	17
12	16	14	16

Page 25
Finding halves of even numbers

Column 1	Column 2	Column 3	Column 4
8	30	10	5
15	33	23	21
1	40	30	33
22	13	31	22
14	24	25	13
4	43	15	44
6	10	45	45
40	3	16	9
12	22	44	15
16	9	14	25
30	2	7	35
40	50	32	31
45	20	41	3
11	11	13	42
23	42	26	23

Page 26
Finding doubles

Column 1	Column 2	Column 3	Column 4
6	12	10	6
30	16	100	120
40	100	90	126
16	160	150	18
18	120	180	80
22	36	38	124
24	62	106	160
60	8	130	26
160	48	28	162
74	198	6	104
48	80	30	88
140	166	128	148
68	44	182	66
144	42	164	122
10	150	102	108

Page 27
Adding multiples of 10

Column 1	Column 2	Column 3	Column 4
110	140	210	120
110	170	250	280
130	180	200	170
130	190	250	120
120	120	110	230
170	160	160	220
120	250	230	260
90	190	220	130
170	170	260	210
160	200	110	210
150	210	200	110
180	280	240	150
150	150	240	130
230	210	190	160
150	210	280	200

Page 28
Subtracting multiples of 10

Column 1	Column 2	Column 3	Column 4
80	50	40	70
140	20	120	110
140	60	40	40
70	50	110	60
110	60	50	140
30	20	40	50
70	50	40	20
90	30	40	30
30	60	50	30
30	80	30	50
80	90	70	70
90	30	60	140
20	50	60	50
160	60	40	80
50	60	70	60

Page 29
Adding and subtracting with multiples of 10

Column 1	Column 2	Column 3	Column 4
140	160	80	180
50	150	250	50
180	80	160	190
90	230	170	110
180	30	110	40
40	150	70	120
120	40	280	50
250	210	20	160
50	40	60	40
150	60	160	250
190	210	60	40
50	90	150	30
30	250	60	190
90	50	230	170
30	200	50	40